My First Book About

Our World

Felicity Brooks and Caroline Young

Illustrated by Mar Ferrero

Designed by Francesca Allen

Contents

Usborne Quicklinks

To visit websites with activities and fun facts about our planet, go to
www.usborne.com/quicklinks and type in the keywords "first book about our world"
We recommend that children are supervised while using the internet.

Our world

Our world is a planet called the Earth.
It's shaped like an enormous ball.
From space it looks a little like this.

The green shapes are land. It is divided up into continents.

Europe is one of Earth's continents. There are six others.

North America

Europe

The blue parts are the oceans. This is the Atlantic Ocean.

Africa

Equator

South America

Antarctica

You can't see the continents of Australia or Asia here as they're on the other side of the Earth.

The red line mark the equator round th middle of the Earth. Yo can't see it in real life

Where in the world do you live?

The continents are divided up into nearly 200 countries. Do you know which one you live in?

Anna lives at 14 East Street. Her street has lots of houses on it.

East Street is one of many streets in the town of Smallton.

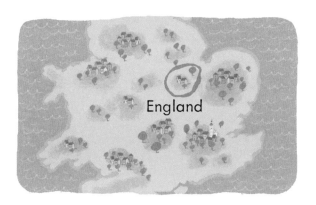

Smallton is one of many towns in Anna's country, England.

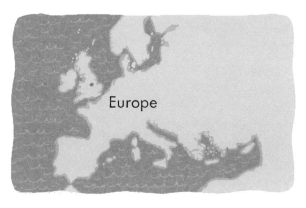

England is one of many countries in the continent of Europe.

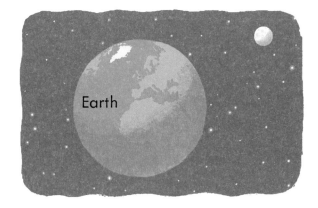

Europe is one of the seven continents on planet Earth.

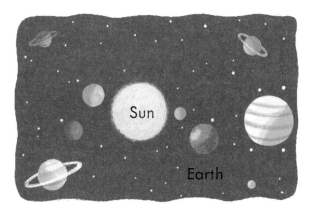

The Earth is one of eight planets in space that go around the Sun.

What's in our world?

Some things in our world were made by people, but many were not. All the things on this page are natural – they weren't made by people.

Match the picture stickers to the words.

rainforest

volcano

grassland

forest

cave

desert

iceberg

mountains

seashore

All these things were made by people. They are man-made.

factories

cities

farms

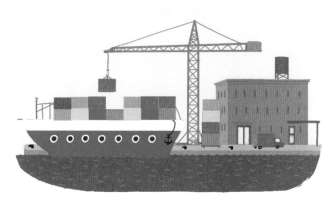
ports and harbours

Which of these things do you think are natural, and which are man-made?

Match the picture stickers to the words.

leaf

hat

book

button

cup

stone

feather

shell

5

The world's weather

The things that make all the world's weather happen are the Sun, air and water.

When the air around us moves very quickly in gusts, it's windy.

When the sky is clear, the Sun can shine on the Earth, so it's sunny.

If it's very cold, the water in rain freezes into snowflakes so it's snowy.

When droplets of water in clouds join together and fall, it's rainy.

Strong wind and rain mean it's stormy. There may be lightning and thunder too.

If it's foggy, tiny droplets of water in the air make it hard to see very far.

What makes it rain?

All water on Earth comes from rain and snow, but there's never any new water. The same rain falls again and again.

cloud

This picture shows why it rains. Add the stickers to finish it.

Sun

3 The droplets join together and fall as rain onto the land, rivers and seas.

2 Some water turns into tiny droplets which rise up and form clouds.

1 The Sun heats the water in rivers, lakes and oceans.

lake

sea

river

4 Rivers flow back into the sea.

land

The seasons

The world's weather changes with the seasons. Each year has four seasons and you can see different things in each one.

Spring

In spring, plants grow and animals have babies. Birds make nests, lay eggs and look after the chicks when they hatch.

Summer

Summer is the warmest season. Trees are covered with leaves, flowers bloom and fruit ripens on bushes and trees.

swallows

When it starts to get cold, some birds fly to warmer parts of the world. This is called migration.

Autumn

In autumn, animals get ready for winter and some hide food. Many trees lose all their leaves and plants stop growing.

Winter

Winter is the coldest season, and few things grow. Some animals sleep right through it. This is called hibernation.

The route of a river

Rivers carry water from the rain and melting snow that falls on hills and mountains down to the sea.

Add sticker labels to some of the things this river passes along the way.

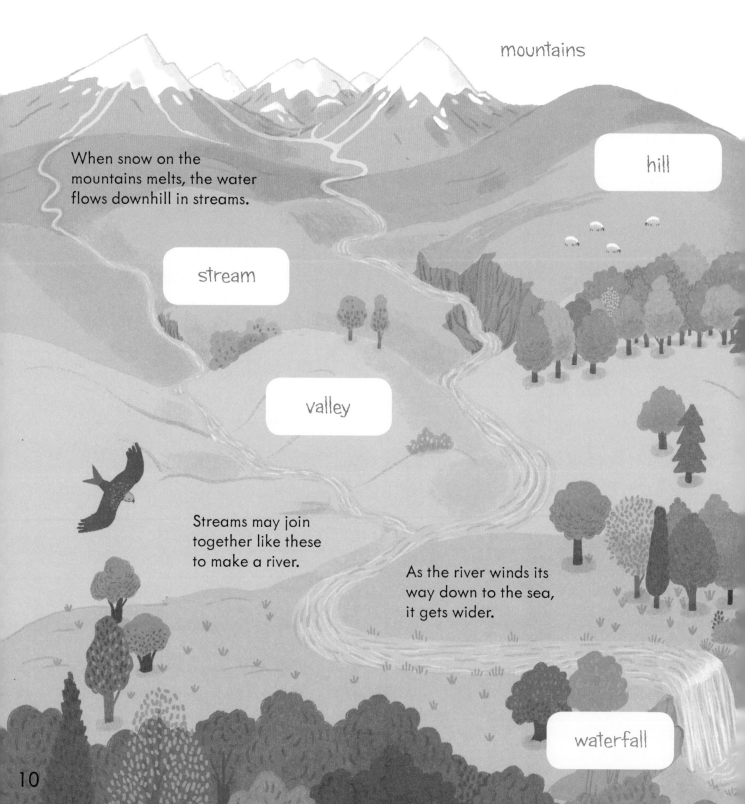

mountains

When snow on the mountains melts, the water flows downhill in streams.

hill

stream

valley

Streams may join together like these to make a river.

As the river winds its way down to the sea, it gets wider.

waterfall

Who lives here?

Rivers are home for lots of birds, fish and other animals. Can you find the stickers to match these?

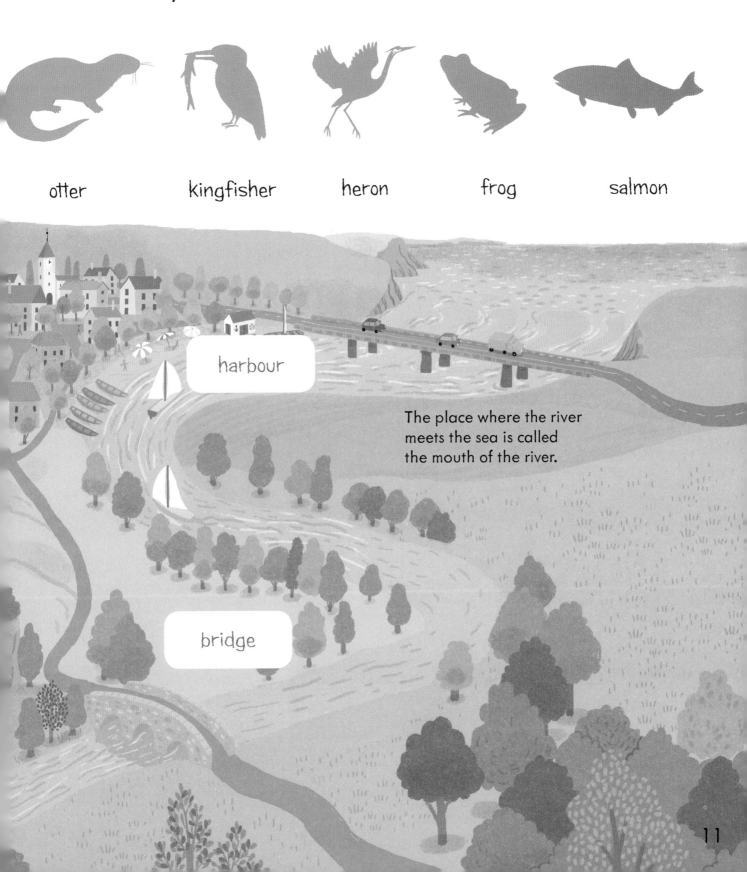

otter   kingfisher   heron   frog   salmon

harbour

bridge

The place where the river meets the sea is called the mouth of the river.

Seas and oceans

Almost three-quarters of the Earth is covered with seas and oceans. They are full of amazing animals and plants.

seagulls

This island is the top of a mountain. Most of it is under the sea.

octopus

turtle

squid

a shoal of fish

ray

The world's oceans

There are five main oceans. Can you add
their labels to this map of the world?

Arctic Ocean

Atlantic Ocean

Pacific Ocean

Indian Ocean

Southern Ocean

dolphin

jellyfish

shark

Coral reefs

In the warm oceans of the world, millions of tiny sea animals join together to make a coral reef, like this one.

Coral reefs are home to a huge number of fish and other animals.

Add stickers to show some more of the fish that live here.

Kinds of coral

These corals grow in the biggest reef in the world, near Australia. It's called The Great Barrier Reef.

See if you can match the sticker pictures to the labels.

fan coral

bird's-nest coral

bubble coral

brain coral

Divers visit reefs to see the amazing coral and fish.

Rainforests

Rainforests, or jungles, grow in the hot areas of the world around the equator. It rains almost every day in rainforests.

A few trees grow very tall. They get plenty of sunlight.

These trees grow close together and shade the forest floor.

It's easy for animals to hide in the thick trees and plants just above the ground.

Hardly any light reaches the forest floor, so it's dark and gloomy.

Where do they live?

Add picture stickers to show who lives in which parts of the Amazon Rainforest in South America.

Birds can fly high above the tree tops and out into the hot sunshine.

Sloths spend their time moving very slowly in the trees above the ground.

Snakes slither around on the ground and up into the trees to catch food.

Shy animals such as this jaguar hide on the shadowy floor of the forest.

Deserts

Deserts are places where little rain falls. They can be very hot in the day and freezing at night.

This hill of sand is called a sand dune.

In parts of deserts there are strange, big craggy rocks.

An oasis is a place with water where plants can grow.

It's hard for animals to live in these hot, dry places, but here are some that do.

This lizard will hide in its burrow to stay cool in the hottest part of the day.

A camel can go a week without water. The hump on its back stores fat.

Fennec foxes have very big ears which help them to stay cool.

18

Grasslands

Grasslands are big areas of land mainly covered with grass. Here are some animals that live on African grasslands.

leopard

giraffe

zebra

hippo

lion

Use the stickers to add some more animals to this picture.

The Arctic and Antarctic

The areas at the top and bottom of the Earth are the Arctic and Antarctic. It's always cold and icy, but some animals do survive there.

Arctic

Antarctic

Add some Arctic animals to this picture.

snowy owl

polar bear

Arctic fox

Arctic hare

baby harp seal

Antarctic penguins

There are no penguins in the Arctic, but millions of them live in the Antarctic in huge groups called colonies. Here are five different kinds.

Emperor penguins are the tallest at about 1m (39in).

Rockhoppers are the smallest at about 50cm (20in).

Emperor parents keep their eggs warm on their feet until the eggs hatch.

emperor

rockhopper

gentoo

chinstrap

macaroni

The world of people

Most people don't live in forests, deserts or other natural places. They live in towns or cities where there are many things to do and see.

Match the word stickers to the buildings in this town.

Opening tonight
Othello

theatre

fire station

police station

museum

post office

railway station

playground

school

hospital

café

library

shop

23

Map of the world

Here's a map of the whole world.
Do you know where you live?.

Match the word stickers
to name all of the oceans
and continents.

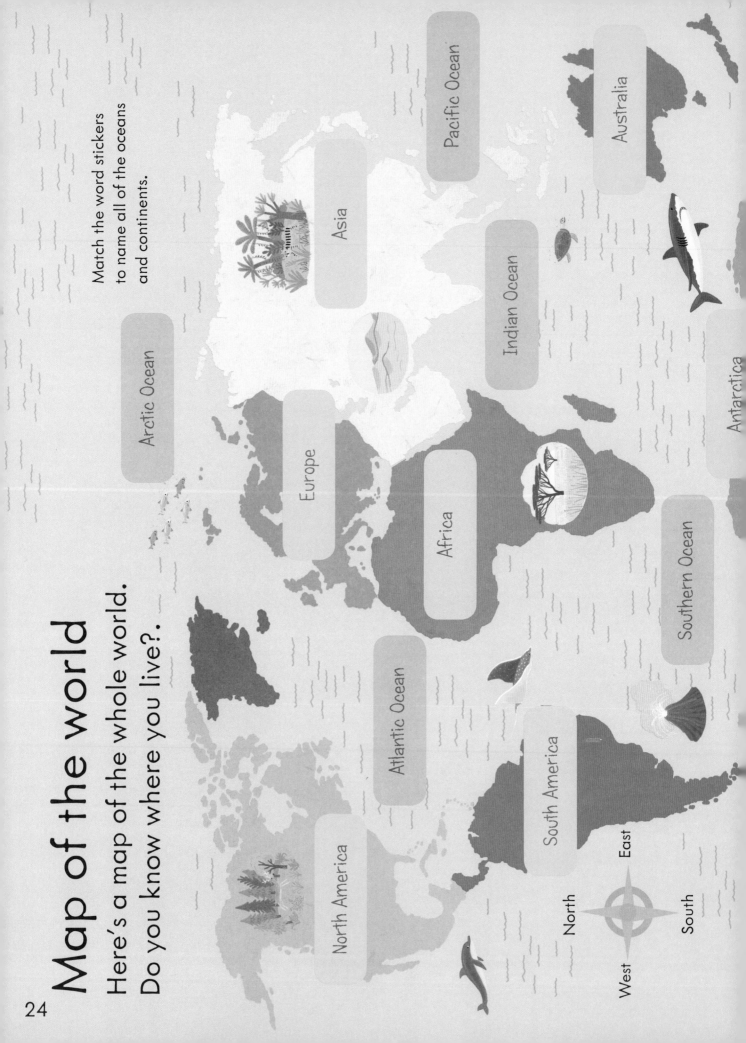

Arctic Ocean

Pacific Ocean

Asia

Australia

Europe

Indian Ocean

Africa

Antarctica

Atlantic Ocean

Southern Ocean

North America

South America

North

East

West

South

What's in our world? (pages 2 - 3)

cave

rainforest

grassland

iceberg

volcano

forest

mountains

seashore

desert

What makes it rain? (page 7)

seagull

the Sun

tiny drops of water

cloud